C902389022

D0552582

DISCARDED

Ladybird Readers

Going Swimming

Series Editor: Sorrel Pitts
Text adapted by Sorrel Pitts

LADYBIRD BOOKS

UK | USA | Canada | Ireland | Australia
India | New Zealand | South Africa

Ladybird Books is part of the Penguin Random House group of companies
whose addresses can be found at global.penguinrandomhouse.com.
www.penguin.co.uk   www.puffin.co.uk   www.ladybird.co.uk

Text adapted from 'Peppa Pig: Going Swimming' – Read it yourself with Ladybird,
first published by Ladybird Books 2016
This version published by Ladybird Books 2018
001

This book copyright © ABD Ltd/Ent. One UK Ltd 2018

This book is based on the
TV Series 'Peppa Pig'.
'Peppa Pig' is created by
Neville Astley and Mark Baker.
Peppa Pig © Astley Baker Davies Ltd/
Entertainment One UK Ltd 2003.

www.peppapig.com

Printed in China

A CIP catalogue record for this book is available from the British Library

ISBN: 978–0–241–31613–9

All correspondence to:
Ladybird Books
Penguin Random House Children's
80 Strand, London WC2R 0RL

MIX
Paper from
responsible sources
FSC® C018179

Going Swimming

Based on the Peppa Pig
TV series

Peppa

George

Daddy Pig

Mommy Pig

Richard Rabbit   Rebecca Rabbit

Mommy Rabbit

swimming pool

watering can

splash

(verb)

5

Peppa and George are at
the swimming pool with
Mommy Pig and Daddy Pig.

Peppa is in the swimming
pool. Peppa loves swimming!

George does not like
the water.

"Come in the swimming pool, George," says Daddy Pig.

SPLASH! George is in the pool. He likes the water now!

Richard and Rebecca
Rabbit are at the
swimming pool with
Mommy Rabbit.

"We love swimming,"
says Rebecca.

George and Richard kick
their feet in the water.

"Don't splash us!" says Daddy Pig.

George and Richard love splashing Daddy Pig and Mommy Rabbit!

"Look! George and Richard are kicking the water," says Peppa to Rebecca.

Peppa and Rebecca
swim in the water.

"Watch us, George!" says Peppa. "We can swim."

Richard has a watering can.

Oh no! It is in the water.

Daddy Pig swims to the watering can.

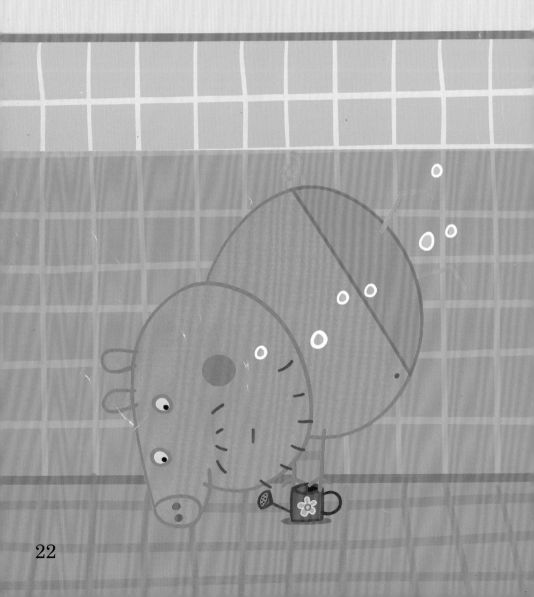

Daddy Pig loves swimming under the water.

"Here's your watering can, Richard," says Daddy Pig.

Oh no! Richard is splashing Daddy Pig with the watering can!

"Don't splash me!" says Daddy Pig.

Peppa and her
friends love
swimming!

Activities

The key below describes the skills practiced in each activity.

 Spelling and writing

 Reading

 Speaking

 Critical thinking

Preparation for the Cambridge Young Learners exams

Look and read. Put a ✓ or a ✗ in the boxes. 📖 ✿

1   This is George.   ✓

2   This is Mommy Pig.   ☐

3   This is Richard Rabbit.   ☐

4   This is Peppa Pig.   ☐

5   This is Mommy Rabbit.   ☐

2 **Look and read. Write *yes* or *no*.**

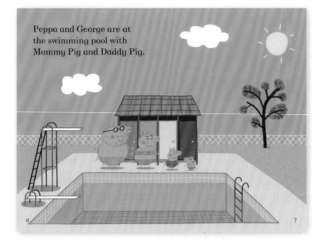

Peppa and George are at the swimming pool with Mommy Pig and Daddy Pig.

1 Peppa is at the swimming pool. ....yes....

2 George is at the swimming pool with Peppa. ....

3 Daddy Pig is in the swimming pool. ....

4 Mommy Pig is at the swimming pool. ....

5 Richard Rabbit is at the swimming pool with Peppa's family. ....

3 **Look at the letters.**
Write the words.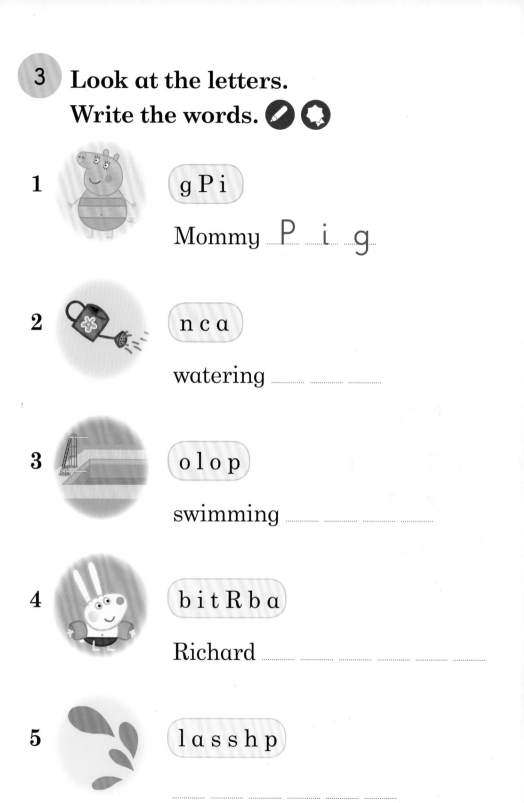

1 g P i

Mommy P i g

2 n c a

watering

3 o l o p

swimming

4 b i t R b a

Richard

5 l a s s h p

4 **Circle the correct sentences.**

Peppa is in the swimming pool. Peppa loves swimming!

George does not like the water.

1 a Peppa is in the swimming pool.

b George is in the swimming pool.

2 a Peppa does not like the water.

b Peppa loves swimming!

3 a Daddy Pig and Mommy Pig are
    in the swimming pool.

b Daddy Pig does not like the water.

4 a George is in the swimming pool.

b George does not like the water.

5 a Peppa loves swimming.
    George does not.

b George loves swimming.
    Peppa does not.

5 **Look and read. Choose the correct words, and write them on the lines.**

"Come in the swimming pool, George," says Daddy Pig.

SPLASH! George is in the pool. He likes the water now!

10   11

swimming   pool   SPLASH   water

1 "Come in the *swimming* pool, George," says Daddy Pig.

2 _____ !

3 George is in the _____ .

4 He likes the _____ now!

6 Ask and answer the questions with a friend.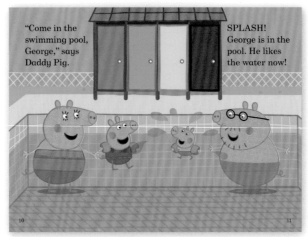

"Come in the swimming pool, George," says Daddy Pig.

SPLASH! George is in the pool. He likes the water now!

10 11

1

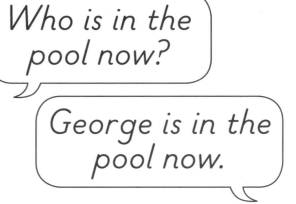

Who is in the pool now?

George is in the pool now.

2 Who says, "Come in the swimming pool."?

3 Who goes SPLASH!?

4 Who likes the water now?

7 Write *is* or *are*.

Richard and Rebecca Rabbit are at the swimming pool with Mommy Rabbit.

"We love swimming," says Rebecca.

1 Richard and Rebecca Rabbit
      are   at the swimming pool.

2 Mommy Rabbit _____ at the pool with Richard and Rebecca Rabbit.

3 Peppa _____ in the swimming pool.

4 George and Mommy Pig _____ in the pool with Peppa.

5 Daddy Pig _____ not in the water.

8 **Circle the correct words.** 📖

George and Richard kick their feet in the water.

14   15

1 (**Richard**) / **Rebecca** is in the water with George.

2 George and Richard **kick** / **swim** their feet.

3 They kick their **hands.** / **feet.**

4 They kick their feet in the **watering can.** / **water.**

9 **Find the words.**

k i j f e e t q u p k i c k m b c G e o r g e l o s w a t e r w x a p o o l p y

feet
kick
George
water
pool

Circle the correct pictures. 📖

1 Who loves splashing?

2 Daddy Pig says, "Don't splash us!"
Who is he talking to?

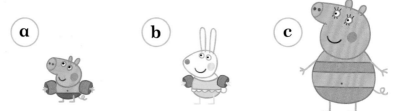

3 Who does George love splashing?

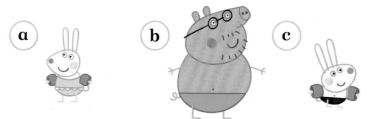

4 Who does Richard love splashing?

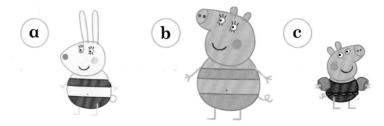

11 Who says this?

Daddy Pig   Rebecca   Peppa

1 "Come in the swimming pool, George,"
says _____ Daddy Pig _____.

2 "We love swimming!" says

_____.

3 "Don't splash us!" says

_____.

4 "Look! George and Richard are
kicking the water," says

_____.

5 "Watch us, George! We can swim,"
says _____.

12 Work with a friend. You are Peppa. Your friend is Rebecca. Ask and answer questions about swimming.

Do you like swimming?

Yes, I do.

13 Look and read. Choose the correct words and write them next to 1—5.

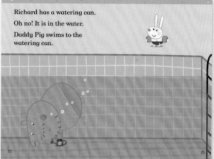

Peppa and Rebecca swim in the water.

"Watch us, George!" says Peppa. "We can swim."

Richard has a watering can. Oh no! It is in the water. Daddy Pig swims to the watering can.

swim   can   George   water   watering

Peppa and Rebecca

1 ....swim........ in the water.

"Watch us, 2 ....!"

says Peppa. "We 3 ....

swim." Richard has a

4 .... can. Oh no!

It is in the 5 ....

14 **Read the questions.**
Write the answers.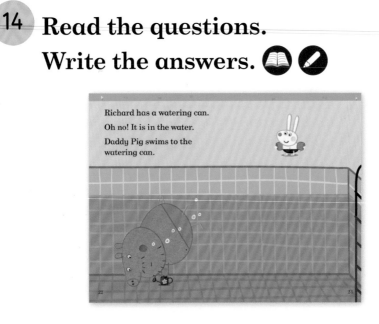

Richard has a watering can.
Oh no! It is in the water.
Daddy Pig swims to the watering can.

1 Who has a watering can?

Richard has a watering can.

2 Where is the watering can?

....

3 Who swims to the watering can?

....

4 Who loves swimming under the water?

....

15 **Order the story. Write 1—4.**

.... "Here's your watering can, Richard," says Daddy Pig.

___1___ Richard has a watering can. Oh no! It is in the water.

.... Daddy Pig swims to the watering can.

.... Oh no! Richard is splashing Daddy Pig with the watering can!

16 **Read the questions.**
Write the answers.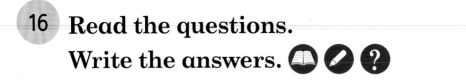

1 Can Daddy Pig swim under the water?

Yes, he can.

2 Does George swim under the water?

....

3 Does Richard want his watering can?

....

4 Does Daddy Pig like Richard splashing
him with the watering can?

....

44

17 **Find the words.** 📖

l	x	u	n	d	e	r	s	y	r	q
k	i	c	k	i	n	g	w	f	a	m
p	d	a	n	k	e	c	i	w	b	o
w	a	t	l	a	k	x	m	z	p	d
l	o	n	u	s	r	a	m	e	o	y
b	i	p	m	d	i	n	i	i	o	a
s	p	l	a	s	h	i	n	g	l	a
w	a	t	e	r	t	y	g	c	v	e

kicking

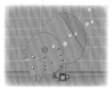

under

splashing

swimming

water

pool

18 **Circle the correct words.**

1 Richard and Rebecca Rabbit are at the swimming pool with

a Mommy Rabbit. **b** water.

2 Peppa swims in the
a watering can.   **b** water.

3 Richard is splashing Daddy Pig with the
a watering can.   **b** splash.

4 "Don't . . . me!" says Daddy Pig.
a water   **b** splash

19 Write the missing letters. ✏️

pp   dd   cc   mm   mm

1 Pe p p a and George are at the pool with Daddy Pig.

2 Mo_____y Pig is with them.

3 "We love swi_____ing," says Rebecca.

4 Peppa and Rebe_____a swim in the water.

5 Richard is splashing Da_____y Pig!

Level 1

Anansi Helps a Friend
978-0-241-25409-7

Cinderella
978-0-241-25407-3

The Enormous Turnip
978-0-241-25408-0

On the Farm
978-0-241-25413-4

Cars
978-0-241-28354-7

Jon's Football Team
978-0-241-25411-0

The Magic Porridge Pot
978-0-241-25406-6

In the Garden
978-0-241-26220-7

Fun with Old Things
978-0-241-26219-1

Fairy Friends
978-0-241-28351-6

Peter Rabbit Goes to the Island
978-0-241-25415-8

Topsy and Tim Go to the Zoo
978-0-241-25414-1

Topsy and Tim Go to the Farm
978-0-241-28355-4

The Fair
978-0-241-28357-8

Daddy Pig's Old Chair
978-0-241-28356-1

Rex the Big Dinosaur
978-0-241-29741-4

Peter Rabbit and the Radish Robber
978-0-241-29742-1

Topsy and Tim Go to London
978-0-241-29743-8

On a Boat
978-0-241-29744-5

Baby Animals
978-0-241-29745-2

The Tale of Peter Rabbit
978-0-241-31614-6

Going Swimming
978-0-241-31613-9

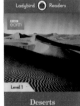
Decepticons in the Scrapyard
978-0-241-31943-7

Deserts
978-0-241-31608-5

Now you're ready for Level 2!